```
HV              Wrobleski, Adina.
6545
.W762           Suicide
1985
         The danger Signs
616.858445
```

Memphis and Shelby County Public Library and Information Center

SSCC - GILL

For the Residents
of
Memphis and Shelby County

Suicide:
THE DANGER SIGNS

Adina Wrobleski

Graphics by Susan K. Lasley

©1984 Adina Wrobleski
5124 Grove Street
Minneapolis, MN.

First Edition - October 1984
Second Edition - July 1985
  2nd Printing — June 1986

All rights reserved. No part of this book may be reproduced in any form or by any means without permission in writing from the author.

ISBN 0-935585-01-X

Printed in the United States of America

"I read your booklets, and it makes this horrible experience more bearable." I.P. Bangor, ME

"Your booklets are excellent. They are easy to read and cover the topics well." E.M. Dallas, TX

"SUICIDE: YOUR CHILD HAS DIED is extremely sensitive and well done." B.L. Tuscon, AZ

"Adina, your publications are superb. You will help many." E.G. Boston, MA

"They brought tears to my eyes. At last someone understands." R.J. Los Angeles, CA

"AFTERWORDS is most informative; your booklets are helpful - especially SUICIDE: YOUR CHILD HAS DIED." J.L. Owatonna, MN

"Reading your booklets gave me a tremendous lift and hope." B.K. Minneapolis, MN

"Your booklets have helped me to understand a lot I couldn't before." A.J. Racine, WI

"Your booklets are the perfect size. I've read some good books on suicide, but they were too long for parents in the early stages of grief." F.S. Orlando, FL

"It's hard to adequately thank you for AFTERWORDS. Now I think of myself as a suicide survivor instead of miserable failure as a mother." G.A. Hartford, CT

"AFTERWORDS is excellent and gives a much needed balance on the subject of suicide and survivors." A.M. Chicago, IL

AFTERWORDS is a Letter for and About Suicide Survivors, edited by Ms. Wrobleski.

Ms. Wrobleski's other booklets are:
SUICIDE: QUESTIONS AND ANSWERS
SUICIDE: YOUR CHILD HAS DIED - FOR ALL PARENTS

"The suicidal person perceives a temporary situation as a permanent loss."

Joseph Richman, Ph.D.

SUICIDE: The Danger Signs

When a family has a member who is mentally ill, suicide may be an ever-present fear. In other families, a suicide attempt or other danger sign of suicide may be the first indication of illness. Fear of suicide can prevent people from getting help.

Self-destructive behavior and suicide can be symptoms of major depression, manic-depressive illness, schizophrenia, and other major mental illnesses, but considering the total number of people who are mentally ill, suicide is rare. Of the 32 million people with mental health problems at any given time in the United States, 30,000 suicides are reported annually. This number of deaths is tragic, but measured against the number of people who are at risk, the odds of a suicide occuring in your family are small.

Of the 30,000 suicides, about ten percent will have had diagnoses of manic-depressive illness or schizophrenia, but the vast majority will result from **unrecognized and undiagnosed major depression.** The remaining suicides result from anxiety disorders, substance abuse, and a very few represent impulsive suicides which can occur, for example, after a sudden catastrophic loss or disaster.

The following are a list of symptoms of major depression, shown beside a list of symptoms of depression as it is sometimes seen in young people. Some depressed young people do not appear unhappy, and look, and are treated, as if they are behavior problems. Their underlying depression goes unrecognized and undiagnosed.

Symptoms Of Major Depression	Symptoms Of Major Depression Sometimes Seen In Young People	
Obvious unhappiness	No apparent unhappiness	
Unable to feel pleasure	Defiant	
Preoccupation with sad thoughts	Rebellious Disobedient Running away Drinking or on drugs	Various Acting out Behaviors Seen
Crying and tearfulness	Refusal to go to school Often failing in school	
Feelings of helplessness, worthlessness and hopelessness	Feelings of helplessness, worthlessness and hopelessness	
Withdrawn and isolated	Withdrawn and isolated	
Loss of energy	Loss of energy	
Self-neglect	Self-neglect	
Loss of concentration	Loss of concentration	
Loss of interest in surroundings	Loss of interest in surroundings	
Loss of interest in favorite things	Loss of interest in favorite things	
Physical complaints (headaches, etc.)	Physical complaints (headaches, etc.)	
Sleep difficulties: insomnia **or** excessive sleeping	Sleep difficulties: insomnia **or** excessive sleeping	
Appetite disorders: Losing weight **or** overeating	Appetite disorders: losing weight **or** overeating	
Loss of interest in sex	Loss of interest in sex	
Thoughts of suicide	Thoughts of suicide	

Not all people who are depressed will always have all of these symptoms, or to the same degree.

Suicide is a process. Suicide is not inherited, but people inherit genetic predispositons to illnesses. For example, diabetes may "run" in a family. Self-destructive behavior and suicide are symptoms of psychiatric illnesses. Most people who inherit a predisposition to an illness never become sick, and illnesses may skip generations. Of those who become ill, only a few will ever become suicidal. Of those who are temporarily suicidal, only a few of them will die by suicide.

Genetics alone do not explain suicide. Emotional and physical environments impact on the lives of people who kill themselves, and self-destructive behavior and suicide can be **learned** as a way of coping emotionally. In about twenty percent of families where a suicide occurs, there are other family members who are self-destructive or who have completed suicide.

The purpose of this booklet is to dispel needless fear, and replace it with knowledge and intervention skills that will lead to correct action, if necessary. The first step to take is to learn the danger signs of suicide.

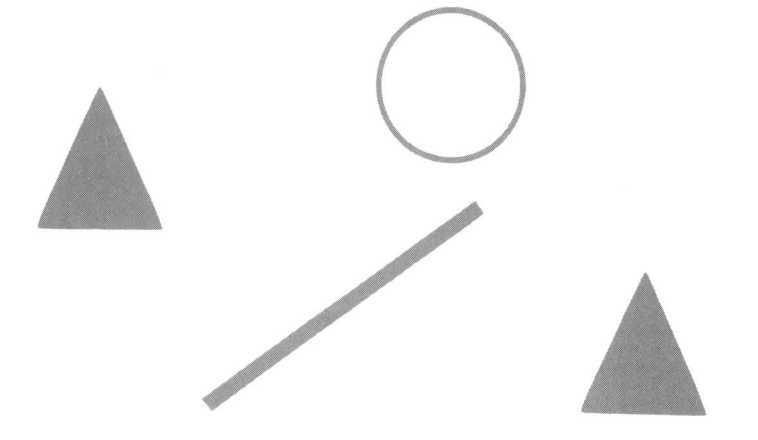

DANGER SIGNS OF SUICIDE

TALKING ABOUT SUICIDE. Studies have found that over eighty percent of the people who complete suicide have made presuicidal communications. Talking about suicide is the single most dangerous sign that it may be about to occur.

GIVING AWAY POSSESSIONS. Some suicidal people will go to a friend, for example, and give away one of their most important possessions. Sometimes they may make a statement such as, "I want you to have this; I won't be needing it any more."

PUTTING AFFAIRS IN ORDER. This usually takes the form of putting business or school affairs in order, getting important papers together, paying off debts, or otherwise settling affairs.

SAYING GOOD-BYE. This usually is not discovered until after the death. Someone at the wake, for example, will mention that just a few days before, the person who died came over, or called, and they had a wonderful visit. Other people then say the same thing, and it is discovered that the person made a systematic effort to contact the people who meant the most to them.

SUDDENLY SEEMS MUCH BETTER. Ironic as it sounds, a person who has been severely depressed, who suddenly seems happy, calm or optimistic, may be at a severe risk of suicide. It can be a short or long term; that is, a sudden improvement may be followed by suicide in a few days, or a person who is gradually improving after a hospitalization may complete suicide in the early months after being released.

Everyone should know these danger signs. If a family member or friend is mentally ill, these danger signs should be discussed and understood by all family members and close friends of the person who is sick. It should be made clear that if any one of them fears or suspects suicide, he or she must report it to the one who has primary care of the person who is ill. It should be treated as an emergency, and immediately discussed with the person's doctor or therapist. Where there is no evidence of depression, everyone should know the danger signs of suicide, as one of them may be the first symptom encountered.

It goes without saying that all homes should be as suicide-proof as possible. **Do not keep firearms of any kind in your house.** Do not keep old prescriptions in your home; throw them away. Monitor medication. It is true that people who are really determined to kill themselves will do so, but most people who kill themselves choose a method that is **available** to them. By suicide-proofing your home, you will make it more difficult for someone to kill him or herself, and should the worst happen, you need not regret that you didn't do all you could.

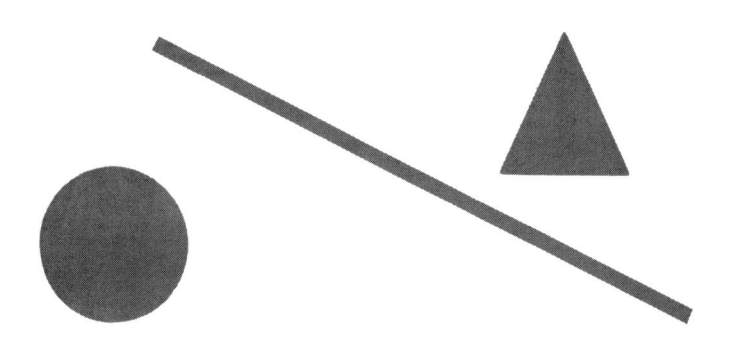

BASIC SUICIDE ASSESSMENT

Basic suicide assessment does not require a professional, but you need to know what questions to ask. If you hear or see any of the danger signs of suicide, the first thing you must do is **ask about it**. This sounds more difficult than it is. For example, if you hear a statement about suicide, or a statement about feeling hopeless, say, "What you just said really scares me. Are you thinking about suicide?" If the answer is "yes," you must follow up by asking, "How would you do it?" If the plan is non-specific, the danger is less than if there is a specific plan plus a deadly method. The most dangerous method is a gun. You must pursue answers. If, for example, you ask what their intended method is, and the response is, "Oh, I guess I would take some pills," then your next question is, "What kind of pills?" When you know what kind, then ask, "Do you **have** any, and if so, how many do you have?"

If there is a specific plan and the means to carry it out, you must remove this means from the home, or out of reach. You may have to search for it. **When a life is at stake, do not worry about privacy and theft issues.** Many parents wish they had invaded the privacy of their children by reading their diaries **before**, rather than after, their suicide. Suicidal people sometimes extract promises from people not to tell anyone about their thoughts of suicide. Promises of this kind must always be broken. The suicidal person may be angry at you for it, but relationships can be mended in the future—if the person is alive.

Continue your assessment by attempting to determine whether one significant thing is causing the person to feel so desperate now. Has there been a loss of some kind? Ask questions such as, "What are you feeling so bad about now?" Pinpointing the anguish and providing reassurance that the person is loved and that these problems are temporary may defuse the situation for the moment.

(If you feel you just can't talk to the person yourself, there are sources of help. You can call a suicide prevention or crisis hotline, and ask for help. Give a brief synopsis of the problem to the person who answers. For example, "I have just been talking with my son, and he says he is thinking of killing himself. Will you talk to him?" They will, and can help you find resources for help.)

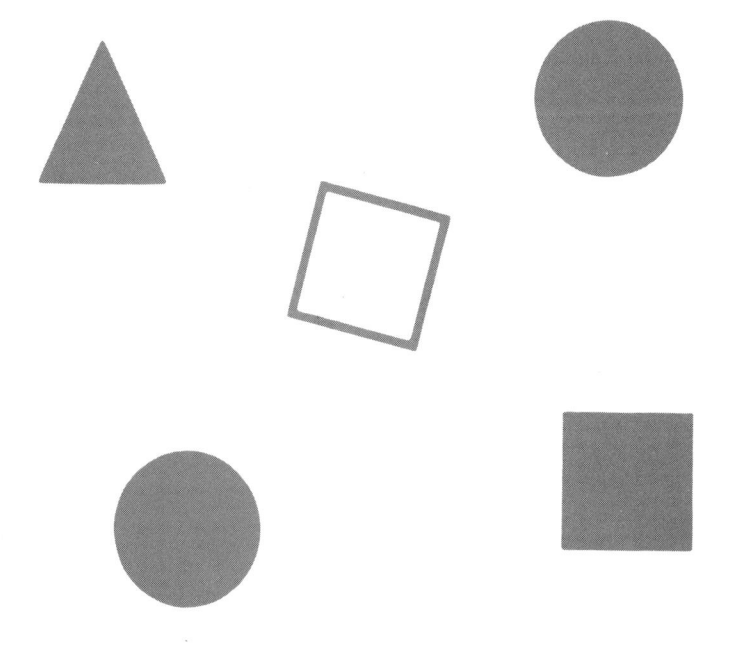

PROFESSIONAL INVOLVEMENT

After your talk, **do not stop at this point**, thinking and hoping the crisis has passed. Do not believe that "talking things out" or being a good "listener" is enough. Don't believe that "loving and understanding" the person enough will prevent their suicide. You must not believe any promises the person may make that suicide will not be attempted.

After this rough assessment of the problem, whether or not it seems very serious, you must seek professional help. If the person is under the care of a professional already, you should call this professional immediately, stating that it is an emergency. If you fear the person is in imminent danger, you can go to any hospital emergency room, but you must give them accurate information and mention suicide when you seek help. For example, "This is my daughter, and she is talking about killing herself." Tell them everything you have found out, because the patient may hold back key pieces of information from a professional.

What kind of professional should you go to? There are many: social workers, pastors, psychiatric nurses, psychologists, family doctors and psychiatrists. If a suicide is imminent, hospitalization may be necessary. Generally speaking, the best person to go to first is your family doctor, who can provide a psychiatric referral and subsequent psychotherapy.

IN REAL LIFE

This advice applies if all goes well. In real life, for various reasons, people may have a bad experience with a mental health professional. There are cases of suicidal people who were turned away from emergency rooms by professionals who would not believe the family's word over that of the patient. If the suicidal person is an adult, some professionals will not see them unless the appointment is made by the sick person, who may have no conception of their own best interests. Some therapists and psychiatrists will not talk to the families of their patients. Do not go to doctors, psychiatrists or other therapists who will not talk to families.

Interview professionals before you engage them. Ask them if they have expertise in dealing with suicidal people. Ask them if they will work in cooperation with the family if therapy is begun, accepting input and information from the family about the patient. Ask them if they will give you advice on how to deal with your ill relative, what to expect, what signs of setback to look for, and what side effects of medicine to look for. Insist on **knowing the diagnosis**, and having it explained to you.

If you have had a bad experience with a mental health professional, **do not give up faith in the whole mental health profession.** There are many fine psychiatrists and psychotherapists.

COOPERATING WITH PROFESSIONALS

Help the person take prescribed medications faithfully. Three general categories of medications are taken for psychiatric illnesses: antidepressants for major depression, Lithium for manic-depressive illness, and antipsychotic or neuroleptic medications for schizophrenia. These medicines affect the chemicals in the brain that determine how people think and feel. **None of these medications are related in any way to "mood altering" illegal drugs, and are not addicting.** Never undermine treatment by letting anyone persuade you or the person who is ill to stop taking their medicine. As the joke goes, don't get your medical advice at the beauty or barber shop. If you have questions about medications or reactions to them, ask the doctor. If you don't like the answers, ask for a second opinion.

The same thing applies in psychotherapy (talking therapy). Psychotherapists often work with patients while they are under medical treatment by psychiatrists. Psychotherapists help people with their life adjustment problems. Ill people need help and support in keeping their appointments, and in implementing the changes in their lives. Psychotherapy alone is not the first choice when a major mental illness is involved. Medicines are usually needed first to get the person to the point where psychotherapy can be of benefit.

Another important thing to remember is that suicidal people are ill, and are not doing or saying disturbing things **on purpose.** They cannot "snap out of it" or "pull themselves together" by their own will.

When the diagnosis is manic-despressive illness or schizophrenia, you are usually looking at chronic, long term illnesses. Some may go into remission, and most will be greatly helped by medicines. Major depression has more variations. Many people have one episode of depression, get well, and never become ill again. Some people will become ill several times in their lives, with many years between occurrences. Some few people will be chronically depressed all their lives.

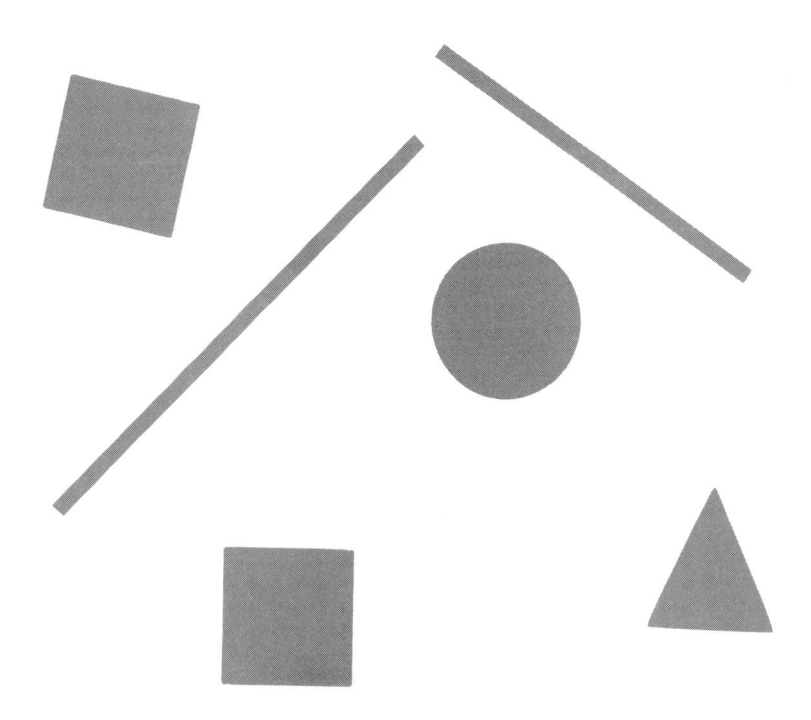

HOPE IN THE FUTURE

There are signs that the taboo and stigma on mental illness and suicide are less prevalent than in the past, and that families of victims will demand that the illnesses of the brain, and the medicines to treat them, be given the priority they deserve in research, public education and help for these families. We need a Suicide Foundation, or its equivalent, comparable to the American Cancer Society or the Diabetes Foundation.

In the future, the brain and its diseases will be better understood. The medicines will improve, as will the education of professionals and the public. For now, families and friends affected by mental illness and suicide must reject the taboo that separates them by silence, and throw off the stigma which dictates a punitive attitude towards families and victims.

Some of the optimistic signs are: the government is giving verbal, if not much monetary support to research into the cause and prevention of suicide; independent scientists and university researchers are investigating mental illness and suicide; and the public is increasingly demanding information as we become aware of the millions of people in our society who are affected by mental illness and suicide.

WHAT CAN YOU DO?

You can join organizations, such as the **National Alliance for the Mentally Ill***, or the **National Mental Health Association****; you can write your legislators and representatives urging them to give higher priorities to funding the research that can lead to the reduction of mental illness and suicide; and you can do many small things. You can refrain from lowering your voice when you say the words mental illness or suicide; you can refrain from using the words "crazy" and "insane," except as slang; you can discuss mental illness and suicide in the same matter-of-fact way you discuss other illnesses and causes of death; you can refrain from putting moral judgments, or "right" or "wrong" labels on mental illness and suicide; you can write to companies or artists who use suicide as a topic of humor in their advertisements or cartoons; and you can tell other people not to make taboo and stigma-based comments in your presence.

We families where mental illness and suicide have occurred must band together to tell society we won't stand for being neglected and treated as if our great personal tragedies put us to shame. The taboo and stigma have separated us for centuries, but the present climate is the most receptive it has ever been. Many of us have received support and encouragement from friends and churches, but we need to build and expand that support. Most people want to help us; they just don't know how. Families who have been affected by mental illness and suicide represent **millions** of people in the population. Truly we are a sleeping giant.

*For information on local affiliates write: NATIONAL ALLIANCE FOR THE MENTALLY ILL, 1200 15th St. N.W., Washington, D.C. 20005.

**For information on local affiliates write: NATIONAL MENTAL HEALTH ASSOCIATION, 1021 Prince Street, Alexandria, VA 22314-2932.

COMMENTS FROM THE EXPERTS

"Optimism about preventing suicide...arises from a feeling that two competing views of how best to achieve prevention may be beginning to merge...between traditional talk-them-out-of-it practitioners in the community suicide-prevention centers that began springing up in the 1950s and biomedical scientists whose more recent research links depression and suicide to a correctable chemical imbalance in the brain." **Arlen J. Large, Wall Street Journal, 8/10/83.**

"The biology of suicide is very new," says **Frederick Goodwin, a clinical psychologist at the National Institute of Mental Health.** "We went for decades assuming that the only tool for helping people was to talk to them and try to sort out their lives. Now, the biomedical factors are of overwhelming importance."

"The profession moved from use of psychotherapy to use of either psychotherapy with drugs or drugs alone...I'm convinced that most of the major mental illnesses have a biologic basis...The current hypothesis is that some people carry a genetic vulnerability for mental illness that might be triggered by events in their lives. It is similar to a theory doctors have about the cause of cancer and diabetes." **Paula Clayton, M.D., Head of the Psychiatry Department, University of Minnesota.**

"We don't know if the mind thinking depressed thoughts causes these biochemical changes or whether the chemical imbalance in the brain is what causes the depression. This is where a Nobel Prize is going to be won." **Dr. Keith H. Brodie, former president of the American Psychiatric Association.**

"Despite many gains, an estimated two-thirds of the people with major depression in the U.S. go without treatment or are inadequately treated." **Abigal Trafford, U.S. News and World Report, 1/24/84.**

ANNOTATED BIBLIOGRAPHY
ADINA WROBLESKI, SUICIDOLOGIST
5124 GROVE STREET
MINNEAPOLIS, MN 55436-2481

Alvarez, A. THE SAVAGE GOD. New York: Random House, 1970. (Out of print, but in libraries. Recommend Part II, "The Background" to understand the treatment of suicides and their survivors in the past.)

Andreasen, N.C. THE BROKEN BRAIN. New York, Harper & Row, 1984. (The most up-to-date information on the brain and how it works and breaks down. Very readable.)

Arrick, F. TUNNEL VISION. New York: Dell Publishing Company, 1980. (To understand the impact of a suicide death. A novel.)

Berent, I. THE ALGEBRA OF SUICIDE. New York: Human Services Press, 1981. (Interesting information on rescue fantasies, and the effect that age, knowledge and experience have with regard to suicide attempts and completions.)

Farberow, N.L. (Ed.) THE MANY FACES OF SUICIDE. New York: McGraw Hill. (About indirect self-destructive behavior - behaviors that are harmful to health over time, but do not cause death immediately.)

Hatton, C.L., Valente, S.M. SUICIDE: ASSESSMENT AND INTERVENTION. Norwalk, CT: Appleton-Century-Crofts, 1984. (Crisis and suicide intervention.)

Hendin, H. SUICIDE IN AMERICA. New York: W.W. Norton & Co., 1982. (Good overview of the subject of suicide.)

Hewett, J.H. AFTER SUICIDE. Philadelphia, PA: Westminster Press, 1980. (Excellent book for suicide survivors.)

Hoff, L.A. PEOPLE IN CRISIS. Menlo Park, CA: Addison-Wesley Publishing Co., 1984. (Crisis and suicide intervention.)

Kiev, A. THE COURAGE TO LIVE. New York: Thomas Y. Crowell Publishers, 1979. (To understand depression and how suicide is related.)

Klagsbrun, F. TOO YOUNG TO DIE. New York: Pocket Books, 1981. (Excellent overview. Best on teenage suicide.)

Krementz, J. HOW IT FEELS WHEN A PARENT DIES. New York: Alfred A. Knopf, 1981. (Includes three children's stories of parents who have killed themselves.)

Kushner, H.S. WHEN BAD THINGS HAPPEN TO GOOD PEOPLE. New York: Avon, 1981.

Maris, R.W. PATHWAYS TO SUICIDE. Baltimore: Johns Hopkins University Press, 1981. (Major study of suicide by white males over 40.)

McIntosh, J.L. RESEARCH IN SUICIDE: A BIBLIOGRAPHY. Westport, CT: Greenwood Press, 1985. (For researchers: contains all bibliography citations on suicide since 1970. Divided in ten chapters by subject.)

Morrison, J.M. YOUR BROTHER'S KEEPER. Chicago: Nelson-Hall, 1981. (A guide for families and friends confronting psychiatric illness. Excellent for understanding major depression, manic depressive illness, and schizophrenia.)

National Institute of Mental Health. DEPRESSION: WHAT WE KNOW. 1985. (Excellent short description of what is known about depression, including various theories. FREE COPY. Order from: Depression Consumer Information Center, Pueblo, CO. 81009.)

Phillips, D.P. & Bollen, K.A. (1981). Imitative suicides: A National Study of the Effects of Television News Stories. AMERICAN SOCIOLOGICAL REVIEW, 47, 802-809. (Abstract: PA, 1983, 70, No. 3590, p. 407).

Reiterman, T., and Jacobs, J. RAVEN, THE UNTOLD STORY OF THE REV. JAMES JONES AND HIS PEOPLE. New York: E.P. Dutton, Inc., 1982.

Sheehan, S. IS THERE NO PLACE ON EARTH FOR ME? Boston: Houghton-Mifflin Co., 1982. (A human story of the tragedy of schizophrenia for the victim and her family.)

Schneidman, E. VOICES OF DEATH. New York: Harper & Row, 1980. (Has very interesting chapter on suicide notes.)

Spillard, A. GRIEF AFTER SUICIDE (pamphlet). Waukesha, WI: Mental Health Ass'n of Waukesha County, Inc., no date. (Excellent for suicide survivors. Send 50 cents WMHA, 414 W. Moreland Blvd., #101, Waukesha, WI. 53186.)

Torrey, E.F. SURVIVING SCHIZOPHRENIA. New York: Harper & Row, 1983. (Everything in simple language you wanted to know about schizophrenia. Excellent.)

Wender, P.H., Klein, D.F. MIND, MOOD AND MEDICINE. New York: A Meridian Book, 1981. (Well written early book on biological psychiatry.)

Winokur, G. DEPRESSION: THE FACTS. New York: Oxford University Press, 1981. (Winokur is early leader in biological psychiatry. Plainly written help in understanding depression.)

Wrobleski, A. AFTERWORDS: A LETTER FOR AND ABOUT SUICIDE SURVIVORS. (For complimentary copy write: 5124 Grove Street, Minneapolis, MN 55436-2481.)

Wrobleski, A. (1985) SUICIDE, CONTAGION AND THE MEDIA, Unpublished.

Wrobleski, A. SUICIDE: QUESTIONS AND ANSWERS, SUICIDE: THE DANGER SIGNS, SUICIDE: YOUR CHILD HAS DIED - FOR ALL PARENTS. Minneapolis, 1984.

Wrobleski, A. "The Suicide Survivor's Grief Group." OMEGA: JOURNAL OF DEATH AND DYING, Vol 15(2), 1984-85.

Wrobleski, A. (1983). RATIONAL SUICIDE: A CONTRADICTION IN TERMS. An address given to the First Unitarian Society, Minneapolis, MN, February 27. (Copies available from the author 50 cents: 5124 Grove Street, Minneapolis, MN 55436-2481.)